ISBN: 978-0-57874-454-4

DEDICATION

TO THE ENTIRE HBCU COMMUNITY AND EVERYONE ELSE WHO SUPPORTS THE HBCU NIGHT MOVEMENT. TO EVERYONE WHO IS WORKING HARD TO FIND EVERY RESOURCE TO EDUCATE THE FUTURE LEADERS OF THIS WORLD, YOU ARE APPRECIATED.

SINCERELY,

DRE

PREFACE

AS A HISTORICALLY BLACK COLLEGE AND UNIVERSITY ENTHUSIAST, I HAVE BEEN FULFILLING MY PURPOSE IN LIFE BY EXECUTING STRATEGIES FOR THE YOUTH TO ASSIMILATE INFORMATION ABOUT HISTORICALLY BLACK COLLEGES & UNIVERSITIES. WITH THE STORY OF HBCU NIGHT, I HOPE TO FOREVER MOTIVATE THE YOUNG GENERATIONS TO BECOME SCHOLARS AND FUTURE LEADERS IN SOCIETY.

"All A's again, Bakari? You are making our HBCU family proud, son!" Momma exclaimed as she served her children breakfast.

Bakari smiled at Momma, then made a funny face at his younger sister, Imani. She giggled and asked, "Momma, what do you mean by "HBCU"?

"Well, Sweetheart, HBCU stands for Historically Black College or University. They were founded to teach our ancestors and they are some of the best schools in the world," Momma replied.

5

After breakfast, Bakari and Imani began washing the dishes.

"You see how much we love HBCUs? You'll learn all about them tonight at *HBCU Night*!" Bakari added.

"Momma told me what HBCUs are, but what is *HBCU Night*?" Imani questioned.

"You'll just have to wait and see," Bakari replied excitedly.

Later that evening, Momma drove Imani and Bakari to the *AMI Arena* for a night of fun.

"Look up at the lights, Imani!" Bakari pointed out.

Imani gazed out the window at the bright lights shining from the arena and the crowd of HBCU families.

"Whoa! And all of those people!" Imani reacted in amazement.

Once they entered the arena, Bakari and Momma showed Imani the *HBCU Fair*. "You see, Imani? These people at the tables are teaching others about HBCUs and scholarships," Bakari said.

"And scholarships are money to help pay for school because Momma got bills," Momma added as she smiled.

Bakari and Imani chuckled. Then, Momma gave a brief history lesson on HBCU pioneers as they continued touring *HBCU Night*.

"Historical figures like Supreme Court Justice, *Thurgood Marshall*, along with legendary writers like *Toni Morrison, Ida B. Wells*, and your favorite hero, *Chadwick Boseman*, all attended HBCUs," Momma explained with pride as they walked to their seats.

"This is the *HBCU Panel.* These graduates talk about fun HBCU experiences and hand out toys for questions," Bakari explained as they listened to the cool stories.

At the end of the discussion, Imani grew the courage to stretch her hand high and asked a question.

Once the panel finished, the tour continued. Imani skipped happily down the concourse as Momma and Bakari cheered her on for winning a *Bison Graduate Toy*.

"Now, this is the *HBCU Party*. You see those people over there, Imani?" Bakari asked. "They are a big piece of the HBCU legacy and are showing fraternity and sorority traditions.

And there goes... Momma." Bakari added, chuckling.

"That's right! Time to show y'all these moves!" Momma replied as she danced in her own section.

After the party ended, Imani, Bakari and Momma high-fived *The HBCU Mascots* on the way to their seats for more HBCU entertainment.

"Alright, Imani, you ready? This is one of the best parts!" Bakari continued with excitement as the trio headed through the tunnel.

17

Once inside, everybody sat on the edge of their seats, waiting. Then, the crowd cheered as the *Mbuzi Kijani Band* marched out beating drums, and playing other instruments while the **Vettes Dancers** pranced onto the court.

"Ouu! I know this song!" Imani shouted as she danced to the HBCU band's tunes.

Before the big game started, a spotlight was given to the HBCU Hero. "Look at the big screen, Imani! That's *Dr. Martin Luther King, Jr.* He was a Civil Rights Pioneer," Momma noted.

HBCU HERO

MLK
JAN. 15,1929 -
APR. 4,1968

"And he graduated from an HBCU *plus* he has his own holiday!"
Imani added. "I want to go to an HBCU and have my own holiday,
too. Can I, Momma?"

"Yes, you can, sweetheart," Momma assured Imani. "The world
is yours."

And as inspiration filled the air, everyone enjoyed the basketball game at *HBCU Night*.

THE END.

ABOUT HBCU NIGHT, INC.

HBCU Night is a multifaceted event and a 501(c)(3) nonprofit organization that was created by the author, Andres D. Martin, to help raise awareness for HBCUs, provide admissions/enrollment resources, scholarship opportunities, and networking opportunities!

TO LEARN MORE ABOUT HBCU NIGHT VISIT WWW.HBCUNIGHT.ORG.

A LIST OF OUR BELOVED HISTORICALLY BLACK COLLEGES AND UNIVERSITIES (PAST AND PRESENT)

ALABAMA A&M UNIVERSITY
NORMAL, AL

ALABAMA STATE UNIVERSITY
MONTGOMERY, AL

ALBANY STATE UNIVERSITY
ALBANY, GA

ALCORN STATE UNIVERSITY
LORMAN, MS

ALLEN UNIVERSITY
COLUMBIA, SC

AMERICAN BAPTIST COLLEGE
NASHVILLE, TN

ARKANSAS BAPTIST COLLEGE
LITTLE ROCK, AR

AVERY COLLEGE
PITTSBURG, PA

BARBER-SCOTIA COLLEGE
CONCORD, NC

BENEDICT COLLEGE
COLUMBIA, SC

BENNETT COLLEGE
GREENSBORO, NC

BETHUNE- COOKMAN UNIVERSITY
DAYTONA BEACH, FL

BIRMINGHAM-EASONIAN BAPTIST BIBLE COLLEGE
BIRMINGHAM, AL

BISHOP COLLEGE
DALLAS, TX

BISHOP STATE COMMUNITY COLLEGE
MOBILE, AL

BLUEFIELD STATE COLLEGE
BLUEFIELD, WV

BOWIE STATE UNIVERSITY
BOWIE, MD

CAMPBELL COLLEGE
JACKSON, MS

CARVER COLLEGE
ATLANTA, GA

CENTRAL STATE UNIVERSITY
WILBERFORCE, OH

CHARLES DREW UNIVERSITY OF MEDICINE & SCIENCE
LOS ANGELES, CA

CHEYNEY UNIVERSITY OF PENNSYLVANIA
CHEYNEY, PA

CLAFLIN UNIVERSITY
ORANGEBURG, SC

CLARK ATLANTA UNIVERSITY
ATLANTA, GA

CLINTON COLLEGE
ROCK HILL, SC

COAHOMA COMMUNITY COLLEGE
CLARKSDALE, MS

CONCORDIA COLLEGE
SELMA, AL

COPPIN STATE UNIVERSITY
BALTIMORE, MD

DANIEL PAYNE COLLEGE
BIRMINGHAM, AL

DELAWARE STATE UNIVERSITY
DOVER, DE

DENMARK TECHNICAL COLLEGE
DENMARK, SC

DILLARD UNIVERSITY
NEW ORLEANS, LA

EDWARD WATERS COLLEGE
JACKSONVILLE, FL

ELIZABETH CITY STATE UNIVERSITY
ELIZABETH CITY, NC

FAYETTEVILLE STATE UNIVERSITY
FAYETTEVILLE, NC

FISK UNIVERSITY
NASHVILLE, TN

FLORIDA AGRICULTURAL AND MECHANICAL UNIVERSITY
TALLAHASSEE, FL

FLORIDA MEMORIAL UNIVERSITY
MIAMI GARDENS, FL

FORT VALLEY STATE UNIVERSITY
FORT VALLEY, GA

FRIENDSHIP COLLEGE
ROCK HILL, SC

GADSDEN STATE COMMUNITY COLLEGE
GADSDEN, AL

GEORGE R. SMITH COLLEGE
SEDALIA, MS

GRAMBLING STATE UNIVERSITY

GUADALUPE COLLEGE
SEGUIN, TX

H. COUNCIL TRENHOLM STATE TECHNICAL COLEGE
MONTGOMERY, AL

HAMPTON UNIVERSITY
HAMPTON, VA

HARRIS-STOWE STATE UNIVERSITY
ST. LOUIS, MO

HINDS COMMUNITY COLLEGE
UTICA, MS

HOOD THEOLOGICAL SEMINARY
SALISBURY, NC

HOWARD UNIVERSITY
WASHINGTON, DC

HUSTON-TILLOTSON UNIVERSITY
AUSTIN, TX

INTERDENOMINATIONAL THEOLOGICAL CENTER
ATLANTA, GA

J.F. DRAKE STATE COMMUNITY AND TECHNICAL COLLEGE
HUNTSVILLE, AL

JACKSON STATE UNIVERSITY
JACKSON, MS

JARVIS CHRISTIAN COLLEGE
HAWKINS, TX

JOHNSON C. SMITH UNIVERSITY
CHARLOTTE, NC

JOHNSON C. SMITH THEOLOGICAL SEMINARY
ATLANTA, GA

KENTUCKY STATE UNIVERSITY

KITTRELL COLLEGE
KITTELL, NC

KNOXVILLE COLLEGE
KNOXVILLE, KY

LANE COLLEGE
JACKSON, TN

LANGSTON UNIVERSITY
LANGSTON, OK

LAWSON STATE COMMUNITY COLLEGE
BIRMINGHAM, AL

LELAND UNIVERSITY
NEW ORLEANS, LA

LEMOYNE-OWEN COLLEGE
MEMPHIS, TN

LEWIS COLLEGE OF BUSINESS
DETROIT, MI

LINCOLN UNIVERSITY
JEFFERSON CITY, MO

LINCOLN UNIVERSITY OF PENNSYLVANIA
LINCOLN UNIVERSITY, PA

LIVINGSTONE COLLEGE
SALISBURY, NC

MARY HOLMES COLLEGE
JACKSONVILLE, MS

MEHARRY MEDICAL COLLEGE
NASHVILLE, TN

MILES COLLEGE
FAIRFIELD, AL

MILES LAW SCHOOL
FAIRFIELD, AL

MISSISSIPPI INDUSTRIAL COLLEGE
HOLLY SPRINGS, MS

MISSISSIPPI VALLEY STATE UNIVERSITY
ITTA BENA, MS

MOREHOUSE COLLEGE
ATLANTA, GA

MOREHOUSE SCHOOL OF MEDICINE
ATLANTA, GA

MORGAN STATE UNIVERSITY
BALTIMORE, MD

MORRIS COLLEGE
SUMTER, SC

MORRIS BROWN COLLEGE
ATLANTA, GA

MORRISTOWN COLLEGE
MORRISTOWN, TN

NATCHEZ JUNIOR COLLGE
NATCHEZ, MS

NORFOLK STATE UNIVERSITY
NORFOLK, VA

NORTH CAROLINA A&T STATE UNIVERSITY
GREENSBORO, NC

NORTH CAROLINA CENTRAL UNIVERSITY
DURHAM, NC

OAKWOOD UNIVERSITY
HUNTSVILLE, AL

PAINE COLLEGE
AUGUSTA, GA

PAUL QUINN COLEGE
DALLAS, TX

PAYNE THEOLOGICAL SEMINARY
WILBERFORCE, OH

PHILANDER-SMITH COLLEGE
LITTLE ROCK, AR

PRAIRIE VIEW A&M UNIVERSITY
PRAIRIE VIEW, TX

PRENTISS INSTITUTE
JEFFERSON DAVIS COUNTY, MS

RUST COLLEGE
HOLLY SPRINGS, MS

ST. AUGUSTINE'S UNIVERSITY
RALEIGH, NC

SAVANNAH STATE UNIVERSITY
SAVANNAH, GA

SELMA UNIVERSITY
SELMA, AL

SHAW UNIVERSITY
RALEIGH, NC

SHELTON STATE COMMUNITY COLLEGE
TUSCALOOSA, AL

SHORTER COLLEGE
NORTH LITTLE ROCK, AR

SIMMONS COLLEGE OF KENTUCKY
LOUISVILLE, KY

SOUTH CAROLINA STATE UNIVERSITY
ORANGEBURG, SC

SOUTHERN UNIVERSITY AND A & M COLLEGE
BATON ROUGE, LA

SOUTHERN UNIVERSITY AT NEW ORLEANS
NEW ORLEANS, LA

SOUTHERN UNIVERSITY OF SHREVEPORT
SHREVEPORT, LA

SOUTHWESTERN CHRISTIAN COLLEGE
TERRELL, TX

SPELMAN COLLEGE
ATLANTA, GA

ST. PAUL'S COLLEGE
LAWRENCEVILLE, VA

ST. PHILIP'S COLLEGE
SAN ANTONIO, TX

STILLMAN COLLEGE
TUSCALOOSA, AL

STORER COLLEGE
HARPER'S FERRY, WV

TALLADEGA COLLEGE
TALLADEGA, AL

TENNESSEE STATE UNIVERSITY
NASHVILLE, TN

TEXAS COLLEGE
TYLER, TX

TEXAS SOUTHERN UNIVERSITY
HOUSTON, TX

TOUGALOO COLLGE
TOUGALOO, MS

TUSKEGEE UNIVERSITY
TUSKEGEE, AL

UNIVERSITY OF ARKANSAS AT PINE BLUFF
PINE BLUFF, AR

UNIVERSITY OF MARYLAND EASTERN SHORE
PRINCESS ANNE, MD

UNIVERSITY OF THE DISTRICT OF COLUMBIA
WASHINGTON, DC

UNIVERSITY OF THE VIRGIN ISLANDS
ST. CROIX & ST. THOMAS, VI

VIRGINIA STATE UNIVERSITY
PETERSBURG, VA

VIRGINIA-UNION UNIVERSITY
RICHMOND, VA

VIRGINIA UNIVERSITY OF LYNCHBURG
LYNCHBURG, VA

VOORHEES COLLEGE
DENMARK, SC

WESTERN UNIVERSITY
QUINDARO, KS

WEST VIRGINIA STATE UNIVERSITY
INSTITUTE, WV

WILBERFORCE UNIVERSITY
WILBERFORCE, OH

WILEY COLLEGE
MARSHALL, TX

WINSTON-SLEM STATE UNIVERSITY
WINSTON-SALEM, NC

XAVIER UNIVERSITY OF LOUISIANA
NEW ORLEANS, LA

LANGUAGE: ENGLISH
RECOMMENDED AGE RANGE: 4-8
PUBLISHER: INDEPENDENTLY PUBLISHED
PRODUCT DIMENSIONS: 8.5 INCHES x 8.5 INCHES
ISBN & BARCODE: 978-0-57874-454-4

Made in the United States
New York, NY
July 19th, 2021

CPSIA information can be obtained
at www.ICGtesting.com
Printed in the USA
BVHW020200240821
615117BV00002B/12